MW00898206

Published by J. Killiebrew, Ph.D.

ISBN: 978-0-578-75353-9

Written by J. Killiebrew, Ph.D

Cover and Illustrations by Lily Quintana R.

Content Creator, J. Killiebrew, Ph.D.

Printed in the United States 2020

There is A Girl Headed to the White House

by J. Killiebrew, Ph.D
Illustrated by Lily Quintana R.

Dedication

This book is dedicated to my niece Lilliana Rose. You are vivacious, bold, fearless, intelligent, and beautiful. You have so much to offer the world. You can be anything you want to be. The world is your table, eat, eat well, and always invite others to join you. Your strength is in how you think, how you love, how you forgive, and how you live. Let your mind always be your greatest contribution to this world. Selah.

There is a girl headed to the White House and this is what she said to me, "Little girl, little girl you can be anything you want to be."

Put your best foot forward, take it one step at a time, the world can take away everything, but what is in your mind. Go to school, do your best, honor your parents, earn respect.

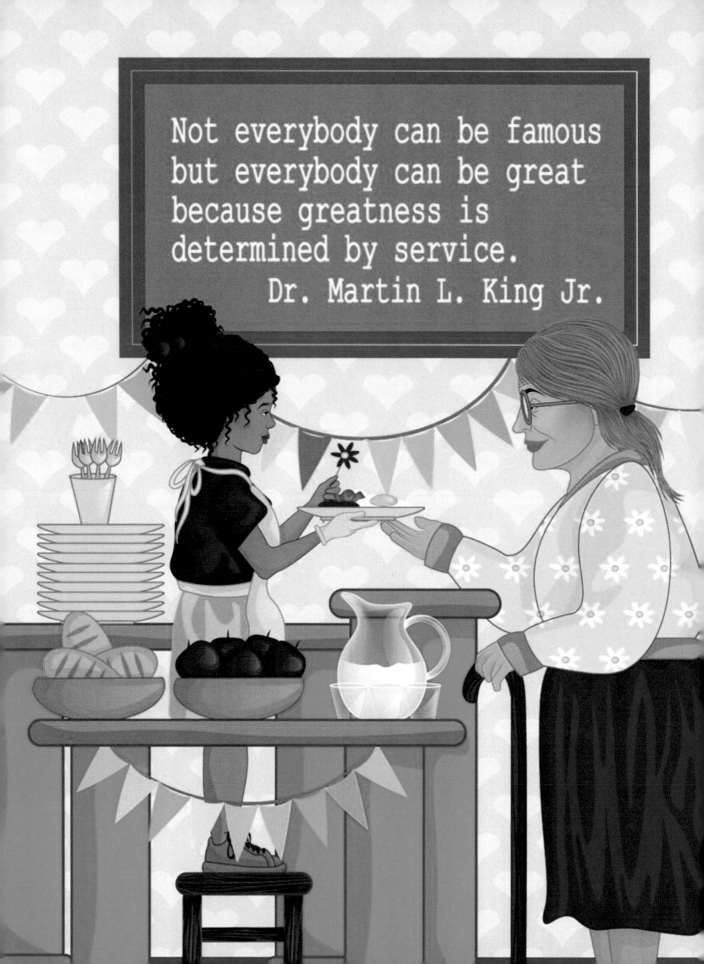

Not everybody can be famous but everybody can be great because greatness is determined by service.
    Dr. Martin L. King Jr.

Study, practice, serve others, and give. Your best example to the world will be shown through the life you live. Make positive friends, volunteer, hold your family near and dear.

Smile often, laugh too, dance freely, always be you. Speak boldly, stand out, learn all you can, and never doubt.

There is a girl headed to the White House and this is what she said to me, "Little girl, little girl you can be anything you want to be."

Always be honest, stay true to who you are, own every room you enter, the world is yours, don't stop at reaching for a star. Always be patient, kind, and love everyone you meet, the world is your table, little girl take a seat.

Find others to help along the way and always remember that you have purpose in every single day. There is a girl headed to the White House and this is what she said to me, "Little girl, little girl you can be anything you want to be."

I look at this girl and I see all of me. She is all that I wish to be. I see my mother, my sister, my aunts, and my grandmother in her eyes. This girl understands that her mind is her most valuable prize.

The sky is not her limit, she can have it all. With her chin up marching forward, this girl stands tall. The girl on her way to the White House, worked hard and earned her way. Nothing was given to her, her mind and her tears earned her stay. Girl, oh girl, continue to lead the way. The future is female and we are here to stay.

There is a girl on her way to the White House and this is what she said to me, "Little girl, little girl you can be anything you want to be."

When one girl wins, we all win.

Made in the USA
Las Vegas, NV
10 April 2021